REVELATION

SPAWN®: REVELATION

ISBN 1 85286 830 9

Published by Titan Books Ltd

42 - 44 Dolben St

London SE1 0UP

In association with Image Comics™

This book collects issues 12 – 15 of the Image Comics' series *Spawn*.
Originally collected in the USA as *Spawn Volume 3*.

British Library Cataloguing-In-Publication data. A catalogue record for this
book is available from the British Library.

First edition: June 1997

10 9 8 7 6 5 4 3 2 1

Printed in Italy.

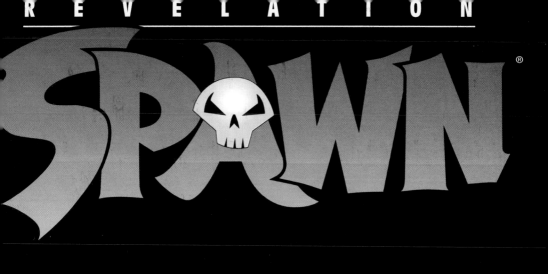

REVELATION
SPAWN

TODD McFARLANE

TITAN BOOKS
in association with IMAGE COMICS™

uestions. Some answered, some teasingly, tantalisingly close to full revelation, others still engulfed in a darkness as impenetrable as that which now shrouds the tormented, damned soul of Al Simmons. And chief amongst the missing pieces from the scattered jigsaw that is the life, death and re-birth of Al Simmons', is who pulled the fateful trigger? Who killed Spawn?

From the Cimmerian depths of a life spent courting and dealing death as an operative for a covert intra-governmental organisation run by the equally umbral Jason Wynn come kaleidoscopic fragments of a past lit at precious, yet elusive, intervals by Simmons' all-encompassing love for his wife Wanda Blake.

It was this love, Simmons discovers, that ultimately led him to sign away his very soul, to strike a deal with the Devil himself.

Now he is Spawn, risen, recreated and clothed in a living, constantly evolving suit; a symbiotic neural parasite that channels and directs the hellish energies that now course through his body.

Destined to lead Hell's army in the name of arch demon Malebolgia, Spawn comes to realise that he has sold his soul on empty promises, tugged and pulled by a malicious master puppeteer.

Wanda, the cherished object of a love that simply would not die, has remarried, given birth to a daughter. The world Al Simmons gave up everything to return to has moved on, consigned his frozen smile to a tarnished frame on a dusty shelf, a case file stamped 'closed'. There is nothing for him any more, and the only things that

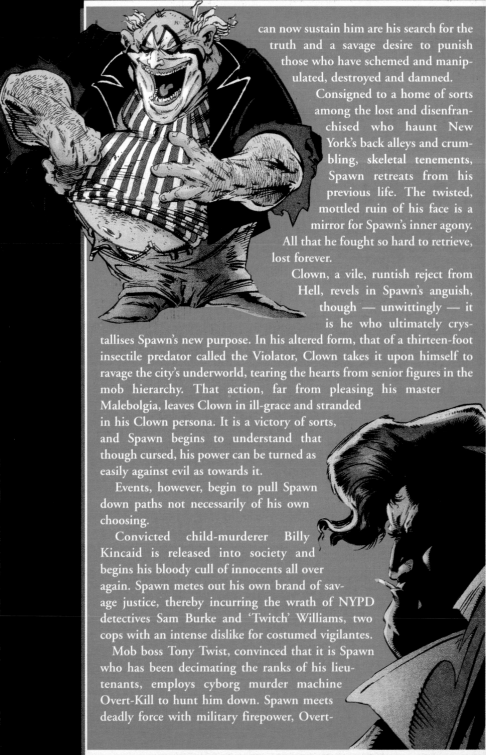

can now sustain him are his search for the truth and a savage desire to punish those who have schemed and manipulated, destroyed and damned.

Consigned to a home of sorts among the lost and disenfranchised who haunt New York's back alleys and crumbling, skeletal tenements, Spawn retreats from his previous life. The twisted, mottled ruin of his face is a mirror for Spawn's inner agony. All that he fought so hard to retrieve, lost forever.

Clown, a vile, runtish reject from Hell, revels in Spawn's anguish, though — unwittingly — it is he who ultimately crystallises Spawn's new purpose. In his altered form, that of a thirteen-foot insectile predator called the Violator, Clown takes it upon himself to ravage the city's underworld, tearing the hearts from senior figures in the mob hierarchy. That action, far from pleasing his master Malebolgia, leaves Clown in ill-grace and stranded in his Clown persona. It is a victory of sorts, and Spawn begins to understand that though cursed, his power can be turned as easily against evil as towards it.

Events, however, begin to pull Spawn down paths not necessarily of his own choosing.

Convicted child-murderer Billy Kincaid is released into society and begins his bloody cull of innocents all over again. Spawn metes out his own brand of savage justice, thereby incurring the wrath of NYPD detectives Sam Burke and 'Twitch' Williams, two cops with an intense dislike for costumed vigilantes.

Mob boss Tony Twist, convinced that it is Spawn who has been decimating the ranks of his lieutenants, employs cyborg murder machine Overt-Kill to hunt him down. Spawn meets deadly force with military firepower, Overt-

Kill is destroyed. Twist, though, is not a man to give up, and so another player enters the arena.

Hell meets Heaven, as Angela — one of a race of warrior angels dedicated to hunting down and killing Hellspawn — takes it upon herself to add Spawn to a tally stretching through the centuries. The prey turns hunter, the angel is vanquished, but the forces of light are many and varied, and their hatred of Hell and its kin is infinite.

An old man named Cagliostro, with knowledge about Spawn that borders on the mystical, appears and disappears, posing more questions than he answers.

But the one answer Spawn wants more than any other remains buried, interred with other restless ghosts that haunt his psyche. It is the answer to the question... WHO KILLED ME?

1

F L A S H B A C K
Part One

MORE APPROPRIATELY, HELLSPAWN. THE OFFICERS-IN-TRAINING OF THE MALEBOLGIA, SENT TO THE LIVING WORLD TO HONE THEIR POTENT, YET LIMITED, SUPPLY OF POWER. THEY MUST FIRST PROVE WORTHY OF THEIR RARE SELECTION AS A WARRIOR FROM THE REALMS BEYOND.

THE LATEST RECRUIT, AND THE FIRST THIS CENTURY, IS LT. COLONEL AL SIMMONS. MILLIONS OF SOULS, BOTH GOOD AND EVIL, WERE BYPASSED BEFORE SIMMONS WAS APPOINTED. HE HAD THE GIFT. THE RIGHT WIRING. THE WELL-TOOLED MACHINERY. DURING HIS FIRST EXISTENCE ON EARTH, HE HAD SHOWN A WILLINGNESS TO FOLLOW ORDERS. TO KILL. TO MURDER. TO SLAUGHTER. ALL IN THE NAME OF DUTY. HE DIDN'T BELIEVE IN THE GREAT BEYOND, BUT HIS ATHEISTIC LEANINGS ONLY MADE HELL'S SELECTION OF HIM EVEN MORE SATISFYING.

YET THE UNBELIEVER CANNOT BE CHOSEN AGAINST HIS WILL. HE OR SHE MUST OPEN THE DOOR TO EVIL WILLINGLY AND WITHOUT HESITATION. THE SURREAL TRAUMA OF DEATH EXPERIENCED BY EACH SOUL LEAVES MANY OPEN TO EXPLOITATION. THE EVIL ONE QUICKLY FOUND THE **CHINK** IN SIMMONS' EMOTIONAL ARMOR:

LOVE.

NOT FOR DUTY OR COUNTRY, BUT FOR SOMEONE. THIS WEAKNESS HAS BEEN THE GREATEST OF ALL AIDS TO ENLISTMENT FOR THE MALEBOLGIA'S ARMY. EASILY-MANIPULATED NEWLY-ARRIVED SOULS WILL BARTER NEARLY ANYTHING FOR LOVE. THEY WILL PROMISE, AND EVIL WILL ACCEPT. THUS, THEIR FATE IS SEALED. THE PACT WILL BE IN EFFECT FOR ETERNITY.

THIS IRONY-- LOVE AS EVIL'S TRUMP CARD-- IS NOT HIDDEN FROM GOD. SOME DAY, THESE TWO POWERS WILL CLASH OVER THIS COSMIC "HOLY GRAIL"-- ARMAGEDDON WILL BE FOUGHT FOR THE REASON HUMANS EXIST IN THE FIRST PLACE...

LOVE.

AL SIMMONS TRADED HIS SOUL FOR IT.

NOR IS THE LURE OF THIS CHURCH, NOW, FOR THE THIRD TIME HE HAS HEEDED ITS CALL, NOT KNOWING WHETHER SOME DIVINE SPIRIT IS TRYING TO HELP OR HAUNT HIM.

HIS STILL-HUMAN THOUGHT PROCESS ALLOWS HIM TO MAKE ONLY THE OBVIOUS PERSONAL CONNECTION...

AT LEAST HE ACCEPTS THE NOTION THAT HIS LIFE IS COMPLETELY OUT OF CONTROL. THE FIGHT WITH ANGELA THE ANGEL WARRIOR, SENT HIM TO PURGATORY, TEMPORARILY DISCONNECTING HIS POWERS. WHEN ALL SEEMED LOST, HE BLINKED, ONLY TO FIND HIMSELF BACK ON EARTH AGAIN, AMONG HIS NEW-FOUND FRIENDS:

NEW YORK'S HOMELESS.

HIS POWERS OBVIOUSLY INCLUDE TRANSMUTATION AND REALITY-ADJUSTING...

UNFORTUNATELY, NEITHER IS AT HIS DISCRETION.

AND WHO COULD FORGET LITTLE **GRANDMA BLAKE.** HER BLINDNESS NEVER SLOWED THAT WOMAN DOWN FOR A SECOND. FIESTY, JUST LIKE HER GRAND-DAUGHTER.

PLEASE, AL. I DON'T MEAN TO PRY, BUT WHY DON'T YOU *MAKE* WANDA TAKE YOUR LAST NAME. SHE WON'T LISTEN TO ME. CURSE HER STUBBORNNESS.

DOESN'T SHE LOVE YOU? ISN'T SHE PROUD OF YOUR NAME? WHAT ABOUT YOUR MOM AND DAD...?

THEY MUST BE HURT.

IT MUST HAVE BEEN THE *FIFTIETH* TIME WE'D HAD THIS DISCUSSION. I TOLD HER THE SAME THING I DID THE *OTHER FORTY-NINE* TIMES. "I MET A WANDA BLAKE. I FELL IN LOVE WITH A WANDA BLAKE. I'VE BEEN *DATING* A WANDA BLAKE AND NOW I WAS *MARRIED* TO A WANDA BLAKE. WANDA SIMMONS SOUNDS LIKE MY SISTER."

BUT WHAT ABOUT THE *CHILDREN?* WHAT ARE *THEY* GONNA BE? *SIMMONS? BLAKE?* ONE OF THEM SILLY *HYPHENATED* NAMES?

PLEASE, THINK ABOUT THE *CHILDREN.*

CHILDREN. FUNNY HOW THAT POINT BECAME MOOT.

I WASN'T ABLE TO GIVE WANDA THE KIDS SHE WANTED SO DESPERATELY.

DON'T WORRY. WE'VE FIGURED IT ALL OUT. INSTEAD OF "BLAKE-SIMMONS," WE'RE GOING TO SHORTEN IT TO B.S.

BIG B.S.! AND *LITTLE B.S.!*

WE'RE PLANNING ON HAVING ONLY TWO.

I DON'T THINK SHE WAS AMUSED. THE DOCTORS SAID IT WASN'T ME WHO WAS STERILE. NOW I KNOW THEY WERE *WRONG.* TERRY-- DAMN HIM-- HE GAVE HER A CHILD.

MY BEST MAN. MY BEST FRIEND! HOW COULD HE MARRY HER?!

HOW COULD HE DO THAT TO ME?! HIM AND WANDA! AT NIGHT! *IN THEIR BEDROOM!!* I CAN'T STOP THINKING ABOUT IT. I FEEL LIKE I'M BEING CHEATED ON.

DRIVING MYSELF *CRAZY.* NEED TO GET A GRIP.

I KNOW. IT'S NOT HIS FAULT. IT'S NO ONE'S FAULT. BUT THAT DOESN'T MAKE IT FEEL ANY BETTER.

I NEED *HELP.* I THINK I KNOW WHERE TO GET SOME.

OUR INVESTIGATION SHOWED THAT ONLY A *HANDFUL* OF PERSONNEL EVEN HAD ACCESS TO THOSE FILES, SIR.

COMBINED WITH THE KNOWLEDGE OF OUR ARMORY HARDWARE PLACEMENT, WE'VE NARROWED OUR LIST DOWN TO THREE POSSIBILITIES.

WHO'S THE TOP SUSPECT AT THE MOMENT?

YOU'RE NOT GOING TO LIKE THIS, SIR.

FITZGERALD. *TERRY FITZGERALD*.

DAMN.

I HAD SUCH HIGH HOPES FOR THE YOUNG MAN. WHAT A DISAPPOINTMENT.

CONTINUE.

OUR DATA SHOWS THAT HE IS HEAVILY LINKED WITH ALL FACETS OF HIGH-PRIORITY GOVERNMENTAL PROJECTS, AS WELL AS CONSTANT INTERACTION WITH C.I.A. AND PRESIDENTIAL FILES. TO THIS POINT HE HAS KEPT A CLEAN RECORD AND HAS BEEN COMPLETELY OPEN TO ANY SECURITY CHECKS.

WHAT'S HIS MOTIVE?

REVENGE.

AS I'M SURE YOU'RE AWARE, FITZGERALD WAS BEST FRIENDS WITH *LT. COLONEL AL SIMMONS*, ONE OF YOUR *FORMER* AGENTS. IT'S OUR BELIEF THAT HE IS TRYING TO GATHER INFORMATION THAT MIGHT BE USEFUL IN A *BLACKMAIL* SITUATION.

YOU REMEMBER SIMMONS, DON'T YOU, SIR?

NEW YORK CITY OFFICIALS CONFIRMED THEIR INTENT TO BEEF UP POLICE PRESENCE IN MANHATTAN'S LOWER WEST IN RESPONSE TO THE SUDDEN RASH OF *VIOLENCE* IN THAT CITY'S BACK STREETS. BESIDES EARLIER REPORTS OF NONSANCTIONED *YOUNGBLOOD* ACTIVITY, THERE REMAINS THE QUESTION OF WHY SO MANY OF THE VICTIMS ARE SUSPECT OF CONNECTIONS TO THE *MAFIA*.

WITH THIS NEW DEVELOPMENT, IT COMES AS NO SURPRISE TO ORGANIZED CRIME WATCHE THAT SICILIAN BODYGUARD *OVERT-KILL* WAS REPORTEDLY SEEN IN NEW YORK LAST WEEK. HOWEVER, OUR REPORTERS HAVE HAD NO LUCK IN DETERMINING HIS WHEREABOUTS.

ACCORDING TO SOURCES CLOSE TO THE MAYOR'S OFFICE, MANHATTAN IS FACING THE GRIM POSSIBILITY OF A *WAR*, SEEMINGL BETWEEN THOSE MAFIA GANGS AND THE MOBS OF DISENFRANCHISED YOUTH WHO PATTERN THEMSELVES AFTER THE GOVERN-MENT'S *YOUNGBLOOD* PROGRAM.

SPINELESS WHELPS!!

THAT'S RIGHT, YOU PUNKS, *YOU HEARD ME!* IN MY DAY, WE DIDN'T RESORT TO SUCH *COWARDLY* STUNTS AS SHOOTING ONE ANOTHER! MIND YOU, I DON'T GIVE A *HOOT* IF YOU WANT TO LITTER THE ALLEYS WITH EACH OTHERS' *INTESTINES!*

FACT *IS,* THAT'D MAKE ME RATHER *GIDDY*. WHAT GETS MY GOAT, THOUGH, IS THAT YOU HAVE TO SHOOT AT *ALL*. YOU WANT TO EMULATE THE GOVERNMENT WHIZ KIDS, FINE! I THINK THAT'S *MORONIC,* BUT WHAT CAN I EXPECT FROM A BUNCH OF TEENAGE *TECHNO-NERDS?!*

CERTAINLY *NOT* INTELLIGENCE.

WHEN *I* BELONGED TO GANGS, WE SETTLED THINGS WITH OUR *FISTS!* YOU COULD SEE THE ENEMY'S EYES. NOW *YOU* USE YOUNGBLOOD-TYPE MILITARY *HARDWARE* THAT CAN LEVEL A *CITY BLOCK* IN ONE SHOT

OH YEAH, WHAT A BUNCHA *FRIGGIN'* HEROE

IN A MAJOR COUP FOR *PARAMOUNT,* STUDIO EXECUTIVES HAVE PURCHASED THE FILM RIGHTS TO MARK CURTIS' BEST-SELLER, *"COURAGEOUS AMBITIONS: THE AL SIMMONS STORY."* THIS UNOFFICIAL BIOGRAPHY DELVES INTO THE POLITICAL ARENA TO SHOW US JUST HOW DEMANDING IT CAN BE, WORKING AS ONE OF THE PRESIDENT'S *ERRAND BOYS*.

FOLLOWING THE HUGE SUCCESS OF CLINT EASTWOOD'S NEW FILM *"IN THE LINE OF FIRE,"* AS WELL AS PRIOR FASCINATION WITH COLONEL OLIVER NORTH AND GENERAL "STORMIN'" NORMAN SCHWARTZ KOPF, IT LOOKS AS IF HOLLYWOOD IS DETERMINED TO RUN THIS NEW GENRE INTO THE GROUND.

THIS JUST IN...

WE'VE RECEIVED WORD THAT THE AGENCY HANDLING YOUNGBLOODS' VERY OWN *BEDROCK* HAS RUN INTO SOME LEGAL SNAGS WITH ANIMATORS *HANNA-BARBAR* OVER NAME-USE RIGHTS.

AL'S MIND EXPLODES. HE BELIEVES IT'S THE ALCOHOL.

IT'S NOT.

THEN SUDDENLY, THE PICTURES BECOME CLEARER.

THE CLUES HAVE BEEN THERE ALL THE TIME.

HE HAD THOUGHT THE COFFIN WAS A REMINDER OF HIS DEATH. IN A WAY, IT *WAS*. BUT IT ALSO MEANT SO MUCH *MORE*.

THE FLAG!

THAT'S THE MISSING PIECE OF THE PUZZLE.

AND THE *SKULL*!

IT SIGNIFIES *DEATH*. NOT THE GRIM REAPER, AS HIS INSTINCTS WERE TELLING HIM, BUT THE *FACE OF* HIS KILLER.

NEWLY-UNBLOCKED IMAGES COME POURING INTO HIS MEMORY'S VOID.

HE SEES THE FACE OF DEATH SPRINGING FORTH LIKE AN EVIL *WEED*, TO CHOKE OFF THE THINGS AROUND IT.

THE FLAG DIDN'T SIGNIFY PATRIOTISM...

IT WAS THE KILLER'S *EMPLOYER*.

THEN... *SUDDENLY, FINALLY*... IT MAKES SENSE. *ALL* OF IT.

THE FACE OF DEATH WA NOTHING MORE THAN A MASK. OR, MORE SPECIFICALLY... *MAKE-UP*

AND THE FINAL PIECE. IT NOW SEEMS SO OBVIOUS.

"HOW COULD I HAVE BEEN SO BLIND," THINKS AL.

"IT'S NOT MY WEDDING.

"IT'S HIS NAME!

"DAMMIT! IT WASN'T CHURCH--

--IT WAS...

"IT WASN'T A CHURCH...

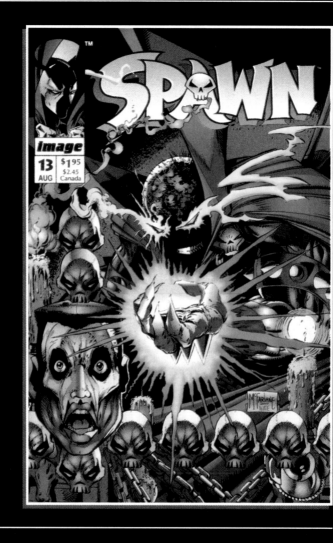

ANOTHER ONE.
THINK OF ANOTHER ONE.

Uh... YES. IT WAS THE SECOND GAME OF THE DOUBLEHEADER. WE'D LOST THE FIRST, BUT WERE TIED IN THE BOTTOM OF THE LAST INNING OF THE SECOND ONE. I'D REACHED FIRST ON A WALK, NEVER WAS MUCH OF A HITTER, THEN STOLE SECOND BASE EASILY. I COULDN'T HIT, BUT NO ONE EVER OUTRAN ME. STANDING ON SECOND, FEELING GOOD ABOUT BEING THE POTENTIAL WINNING RUN, I LOOKED OVER TO BEHIND THE THIRD BASE DUGOUT WHERE WANDA WAS SITTING. SHE SMILED AND STOOD UP SO I COULD SEE HER. THE NEXT BATTER SINGLED TO CENTER, AND I WAS OFF. UNFORTUNATELY, THEIR FIELDER HAD A ROCKET FOR AN ARM. THE BALL, THE CATCHER AND I ARRIVED AT HOME ALL AT THE SAME INSTANT. I WAS OUT, IN MORE WAYS THAN ONE. WHEN THE DUST FROM THE COLLISION HAD CLEARED, THEY HAD TO CARRY ME OFF THE FIELD. I HAD BROKEN MY ANKLE. DON'T EVEN REMEMBER IF WE HAD WON THAT GAME 'CAUSE THE BEST PART CAME AFTER.

ON THE WAY BACK FROM THE HOSPITAL, WANDA SAT CLOSE TO ME. SHE FELT SORRY FOR ME THAT I WOULDN'T GET TO PLAY BALL ANYMORE. ME, TOO, I GUESS. OTHER THAN FIGHT AND KILL, BASEBALL WAS THE ONLY OTHER THING I DID WELL.

BUT I STILL REMEMBER LIKE IT WAS YESTERDAY HOW WANDA CARED FOR AND PAMPERED ME SO I WOULDN'T BE IN PAIN. THAT NIGHT WE MADE LOVE 'TIL THE SUN STARTED COMING UP. MY FOOT STILL THROBBING, SHE MADE ME FORGET EVERYTHING. HER TOUCH EASED MY MIND AND DROVE ME CRAZY AT THE SAME TIME. AND THAT NIGHT, OUR LOVING EACH OTHER, IT WAS ALL SO PERFECT. SO VERY, VERY PERFECT.

ALL THAT'S GONE NOW.

SO I HAVE TO KEEP REMINDING MYSELF OF WHAT HE STOLE. HAVE TO KEEP TELLING MYSELF THESE STORIES. OVER AND OVER. BUILD UP MY RAGE. MY HATE.

PiNG

THE MORE ANGRY I AM, THE LESS I'LL NEED TO RELY ON MY POWERS. CAN'T AFFORD TO USE THEM UNLESS IT'S ABSOLUTELY NECESSARY. I SOMEHOW SENSE THE DRAINAGE. HOW I'VE FOOLISHLY USED ABOUT TWENTY PERCENT ALREADY. IT'S CLEAR THAT I HAVE TO COUNT ON **MYSELF**. **NOT** THESE POWERS.

PiNG

WHAT'S IMPORTANT IS WANDA!
I HAVE TO FOCUS ON THAT.

Tek
Tek
Tek

THE DEVIL TOLD ME THAT ONCE MY POWER IS EXHAUSTED I'LL BE BANISHED FROM EARTH FOREVER. I'D MUCH RATHER GET WANDA BACK, SOLVE MY PROBLEMS, AND NOT USE THESE POWERS AS A CRUTCH.

PiNG

IT'S ALMOST LIKE BEING HUMAN AGAIN.

POK POK POK P

C'MON! C'MON! **C'MON!**

POK Po

KILL 'EM! GET HIM! GET HIM! YEA!

SINCE I'M **NOT**, IT'S TIME TO NAIL THE SCUMBAG WHO HELPED ME INTO THIS BIZARRE SITUATION.

BZiNG

C'MON. C'MON. C'MON. C'MON. C'MON.

THIS SADISTIC GAME.

CHAPEL.

USED TO CALL HIM A FRIEND... ONCE. HAD A FEW LAUGHS TOGETHER.

THEN HE CHANGED. BECAME JUST LIKE ME. OR MAYBE I BECAME LIKE HIM. DOESN'T MATTER NOW.

I'D HEARD HE WAS BEING CONSIDERED AS A RECRUIT FOR THE YOUNGBLOOD PROGRAM. SEEMED LIKE THIS SENT HIM ON A GLORY STREAK TRYING TO PROVE HIS WORTH TO THE BRASS. ALWAYS READY FOR ACTION. ALWAYS READY TO KILL. JUST LIKE ME. FUNNY HOW HIRED ASSASSINS LIKE US COULD FIND DEATH TO BE THE COMMON LINK TO OUR ADMIRATION FOR EACH OTHER.

DEATH.

THE ONE THING WE COULD ALWAYS TALK ABOUT OVER A BEER.

AND WOMEN.

EVERY TIME I SAW HIM, HE HAD ONE OR TWO ALL OVER HIM. "THE DON JUAN OF KILLERS," I CALLED HIM. NEVER DATED ANY OF THEM, JUST GOT LAID THEN TOSSED THEM ASIDE. HE SAID RELATIONSHIPS WERE TOO MUCH TROUBLE.

HE EVEN OFFERED TO TAKE WANDA OFF MY HANDS ONCE A WEEK IF I GOT TIRED OF HER. THE PIG KNEW HOW MUCH I LOVED HER. DIDN'T SEEM TO MATTER, HE ACTUALLY THOUGHT HE'D BE DOING ME A FAVOR.

AW **CRUD!**

NOT ANOTHER ONE?!

CHAPEL DID ME **ONE** FAVOR, THOUGH. DURING HIS REVIEW PERIOD BEFORE HIS INDUCTION INTO YOUNGBLOOD, HE BROUGHT ME TO WASHINGTON, D.C., TO SEE THE GROUP'S CENTRAL HEADQUARTERS.

ESPECIALLY NOT NOW!

THE YOUNGBLOOD PROGRAM HAD BEEN INTERESTED IN ME AS A CANDIDATE. I GUESS THEY WANTED TO SCHMOOZE ME A BIT. LUCKY FOR ME. I GOT TO LEARN THE BASIC LAYOUT OF THE JOINT. IT'S NOT CHANGED ALL THAT MUCH OVER THE LAST FIVE YEARS.

I JUST DON'T BELIEVE IT!

THIS IS THE HUNDREDTH ONE I'VE BROKE ALREADY.

CAN'T THEY GET IT RIGHT? I MEAN, *JEEZ*, THEY CAN PUT A MAN ON THE MOON, BUT THEY CAN'T FIGURE OUT HOW TO BUILD A HAND-HELD TOUGH ENOUGH FOR ME.

THE PLACE IS STILL RIGGED WITH HEAT SENSORS. ANYTHING EVEN REMOTELY HUMAN CAN BE DETECTED. MY BODY DOESN'T TRIP THE ALARM, WHICH MEANS I'M NOT "REMOTELY HUMAN."

NO GREAT SURPRISE THERE.

BY HIDING IN A NEWLY-EMPTIED CANNISTER AMONG SUPPLIES BEING STORED, IT WAS AMAZINGLY EASY TO BE DELIVERED TO THE PROPER LEVEL. I'M LEFT TO WAIT FOR HIS RETURN.

DAYS. WEEKS. HE WOULD HAVE TO RETURN SOMETIME.

I WANTED TO BE THERE.

PLUS, THEY *DOCK* ME EVERY TIME ONE BREAKS.

NICE *INCENTIVE* PROGRAM. AIN'T *MY* FAULT I GOT STUMPS FOR FINGERS.

THEY HAD A *HEART ATTACK* WHEN I ASKED FOR AN ARCADE GAME.

SO I SAT, AND AS EACH DAY PASSED, MY HATED SOFTENED A BIT. I THEN BEGAN TO TELL MYSELF ABOUT WANDA, REMEMBERING THE GREAT TIMES WE HAD. THE SPECIAL MOMENTS. EACH THING I CAN RECALL ENHANCES THE MOOD.

MY ANGER GROWS AGAIN.

ONE FINAL REMINDER BEFORE I TAKE HIM OUT.

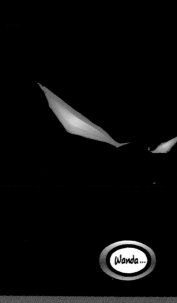

Wanda...

SLAM

THE DEAFENING SOUND OF STEEL RAMMING STEEL **STARTLES** THE THREE YOUNGBLOOD MEMBERS. AT THE DOOR, THEY SEE A FIGURE STANDING POISED FOR THE CHALLENGE. HE DOESN'T MOVE A MUSCLE AS HE CALMLY SCANS THE, CONSIDERING HOW TO USE IT ALL TO HIS ADVANTAGE. ALTHOUGH HE DOESN'T MOVE, HIS CAPE AND CHAINS SEEM TO FLIT ABOUT, SNAPPING LIKE CAGED **ANIMALS** GETTING READY TO FEAST.

HE SPOTS CHAPEL NO MORE THAN THIRTY FEET AWAY, AND HIS **HEART**, IF THAT'S TRULY WHAT IT IS, SKIPS A BEAT. AND YET, HE DOES NOT MOVE. HE HAS DECIDED THAT ANY ACTION WITH THESE YOUNGBLOOD MIGHT BE A DRAIN ON HIS POWERS. BESIDES, IT'S ONLY **ONE** OF THE THREE HE'S CONCERNED WITH.

THOUGH HE WISHES NOT TO WASTE ANY MORE OF HIS PRECIOUS NEW POWERS, HE KNOWS HE HAS NO CHOICE.

MAKE A **MOVE**, MISTER, AND I'LL HAVE TWENTY AGENTS ON YOUR BACK. DON'T KNOW HOW YOU GOT IN, BUT YOU'RE **NOT** GOING TO WALK OUT.

EAM LEADER HAFT COMMANDS THE RESPECT OF THOSE HE LEADS AND THOSE HE FIGHTS. NO SUCH LUCK WITH **THIS** DEAD SOLDIER.

MAKE YOUR MOVE.

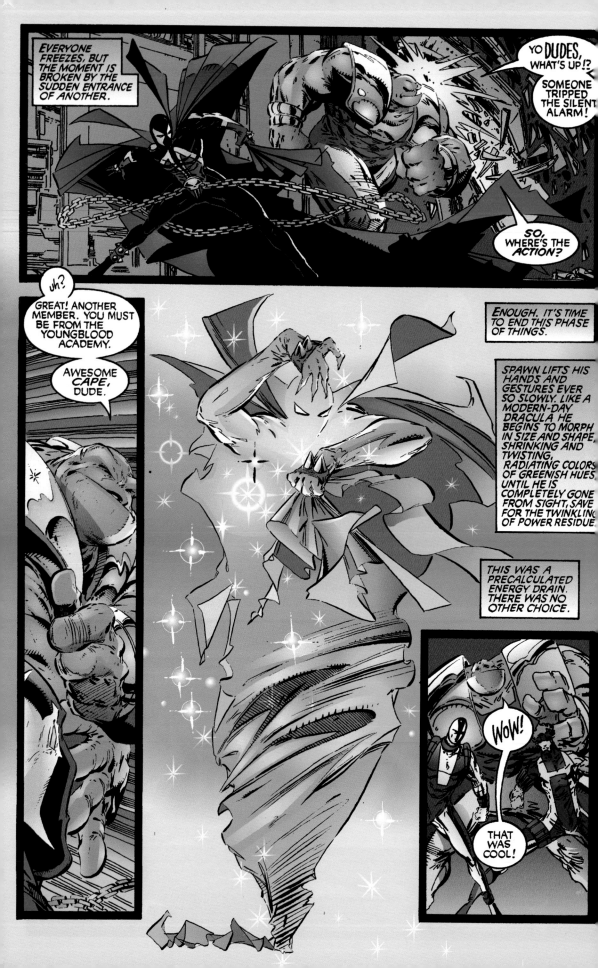

IT'S LATE FOR **TERRY FITZGERALD** AND **WANDA BLAKE.** MOST OF THEIR NEIGHBORS IN THE NEW YORK SUBURB OF QUEENS HAVE BEEN ASLEEP FOR HOURS, NESTLED IN WARM BEDS.

TERRY WISHES HE WAS DOING LIKEWISE.

AS IT IS, HE STANDS, STARING OUT THE WINDOW, NERVOUSLY FIDGETING WITH THE CURTAIN STRING. THE CAUSE OF HIS RESTLESS-NESS: A NONE-TOO-SUBTLE THREAT OF HARM TO HIS FAMILY... FROM HIS OWN AGENCY.

AS AN AGENT OF THE **UNITED STATES SECURITY GROUP** (U.S.S.G.) HE'S ALWAYS FACED THE POSSIBILITY OF DANGER. TERRY DISTANCED HIMSELF FROM THAT SIDE OF THINGS YEARS AGO WHEN HE SHIFTED OVER TO ITS INTER-CULTURAL LIASON UNIT.

AFTER WHAT HAPPENED TO AL, HE NEEDED A BREAK FROM FRONT-LINE ACTIVITY.

HE THOUGHT HE'D FINALLY GOTTEN IT.

THIS MORNING'S THREAT* SAYS OTHERWISE. HE KNOWS THE SECURITY GROUP DOESN'T MUSCLE ITS OWN UNLESS THEY HAVE SOMETHING VERY SERIOUS.

FOR THE LIFE OF HIM, HE CAN'T IMAGINE WHAT THAT CAN BE. THAT DOESN'T MATTER.

*LAST ISSUE--Tom

THAT THEY EVEN IMAGINE A PROBLEM IS DISASTER ENOUGH. NOW HE MUST TRY TO FIND SOME ANSWERS BEFORE THINGS GET REALLY UGLY.

FIND. DETERMINE. FORMULATE. SOLVE. THESE ARE THE FOUR BASIC POINTS OF HIS TRAINING. IT SEEMS THEY LEFT ONE OUT:

Terry, is something wrong?

PROTECT.

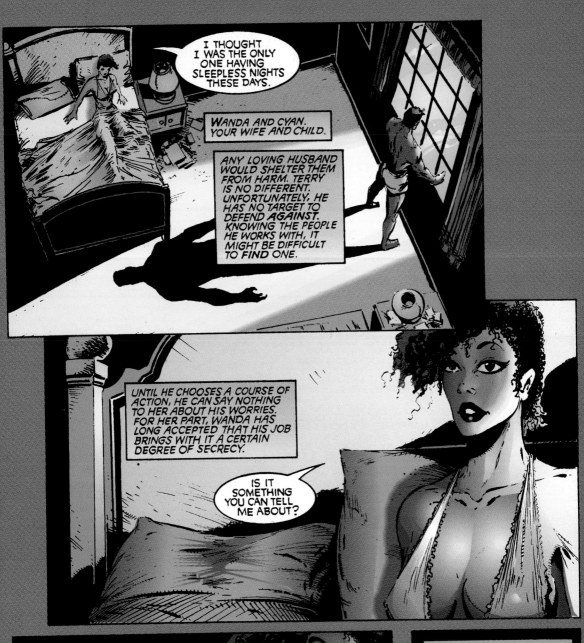

I THOUGHT I WAS THE ONLY ONE HAVING SLEEPLESS NIGHTS THESE DAYS.

WANDA AND CYAN. YOUR WIFE AND CHILD.

ANY LOVING HUSBAND WOULD SHELTER THEM FROM HARM. TERRY IS NO DIFFERENT. UNFORTUNATELY, HE HAS NO TARGET TO DEFEND *AGAINST*. KNOWING THE PEOPLE HE WORKS WITH, IT MIGHT BE DIFFICULT TO *FIND* ONE.

UNTIL HE CHOOSES A COURSE OF ACTION, HE CAN SAY NOTHING TO HER ABOUT HIS WORRIES. FOR HER PART, WANDA HAS LONG ACCEPTED THAT HIS JOB BRINGS WITH IT A CERTAIN DEGREE OF SECRECY.

IS IT SOMETHING YOU CAN TELL ME ABOUT?

NO.

NOT YET.

I'M GOING TO CHECK ON CYAN.

AS HE GAZES AT HIS DAUGHTER'S INNOCENT FACE, HE WONDERS HOW MUCH TIME IS LEFT BEFORE SHE LEARNS THE CRUELTY THAT PEOPLE DO TO EACH OTHER.

...VERNMENT OFFICIALS CONFIRMED TODAY ...T CASUALTIES IN THE U.S./BOTSWANA ...NFLICT INCLUDE LT. COL. AL SIMMONS. HE ...S BEST KNOWN FOR THE COURAGE HE SHOWED ...ILE THWARTING AN ASSASSINATION ATTEMPT ... THE FORMER PRESIDENT.

...HOUGH NO DETAILS WERE GIVEN, A ...ATEMENT READ BY THE WHITE HOUSE PRESS ...CRETARY SAID THAT HE DIED "DEFENDING ... NATION."

...SIMMONS WAS AMONG THAT ELITE BRANCH WHO ...ACTIVITIES WERE COVERT BUT BROADLY DEFINED ..."UPHOLDING THE SECURITY AND INTERESTS OF T ...UNITED STATES." SERVICES WILL BE HELD LATER ...WEEK AT ARLINGTON NATIONAL CEMETARY IN VIR ...BOTH THE PRESIDENT AND VICE-PRESIDENT ARE ...EXPECTED TO ATTEND, AS WELL AS OFFICERS F ...ALL BRANCHES OF THE ARMED SERVICES.

...SIMMONS' WIDOW, WANDA BLAKE, IS IN SECLU ...AND UNAVAILABLE FOR COMMENT.

1987

...Y, LET'S SEE IF I GOT THIS STRAIGHT!

...Y-THREE U.S. SOLDIERS HAVE BEEN KILLED SO ...IN THE U.S./BOTSWANA CONFLICT, BUT THE ...ERNMENT SINGLES OUT *JUST ONE* OF THEM ...OLD UP AS A GLOWING EXAMPLE OF TRUTH, ...ICE AND THE AMERICAN WAY?!

...T ABOUT THE *OTHER* FORTY-TWO DEAD ...CERS? IS ONLY *SIMMONS* TO BE GRANTED ...THOOD?

OR IS THERE SOMETHING *MORE* HERE?

CALL ME A CYNIC, BUT IS IT *JUST* COINCIDENCE THA PRESIDENT IS PULLING AT OUR HEART-STRINGS AN VOWING TO BUILD U.S. ACTIVITY IN THIS WAR *JUS* THE POLLS SHOW HIS POPULARITY AT ROCK BOTTO

NICE *MOVE*, MR. PRESIDENT. *GREAT* TIMING. NOT LIKE A GOOD *WAR* AND A DEAD *HERO* TO HELP BOLSTER YOUR STANDING. THEN AGAIN, I COULD READING *TOO MUCH* INTO THIS.

...Y, WE MARK THE PASSING OF A SOLDIER AS ...UELY SIGNIFICANT IN THE ARMED FORCES ...E WAS IN THE *MEDIA*.

...OL. AL SIMMONS, WHO JUST TWO YEARS AGO ...VOTED ONE OF OUR "TEN SEXIEST MEN" BY *PEOPLE* ...AZINE, HAS BEEN LESS PROMINENT THIS PAST ... THOUGH THIS CHARISMATIC GENTLEMAN ...HT FOR OUR SAFETY EVERY DAY, IT WAS HIS ...ERY DURING THE HINCKLEY INCIDENT THAT ...KED HIM IN OUR MEMORIES.

UNCONFIRMED REPORTS SAY THAT SIMMONS WAS CAUGHT IN AN ENEMY GROUND SWEEP AND TRIE VALIANTLY TO DRAW FIRE AWAY FROM HIS FELLO SOLDIERS.

IT IS SUCH ACTS OF COURAGE THAT MAKE US ALL PROUD OF THE WAR EFFORT IN BOTSWANA. "LT. C SIMMONS, *THOUGH VERY SPECIAL IN HIS OWN RIG CONSIDERED HIMSELF AN EQUAL TO ANY AND ALL W WOULD PUT THEIR LIVES ON THE LINE FOR FREEDOM DEMOCRACY,*" SAID A PENTAGON SPOKESMAN.

MAYBE IT'S *YOU* AND MAYBE IT'S *NOT.* NEVER COULD STOMACH YOUR *WHINING* ALL THE TIME...

...TRYING TO *FIX* EVERYTHING.

YOU ALWAYS *WERE* THE GOODIE-TWO-SHOES. THINK *YOU'RE* SCREWED?!

--THEN **DAMN** YOU!

IT WAS *ME* WHO TOOK THE SERUM, NOT *YOU!* *I'M* THE ONE POISONED WITH *H.I.V.!*

CHTCH

SO **SCREW** YOUR SOB STORY!

How pitiful you've become.

I DIDN'T TAKE THE SERUM BECAUSE WANDA AND I WERE TRYING TO *CONCEIVE.*

SO YOU BELIEVE WHAT YOU WANT. I DON'T *CARE.* BUT IT *IS* ME...

...BACK FROM THE *DEAD.*

WITH MORE POWER THAN I NEED...

...BUT LITTLE ELSE.

YOU DON'T *SCARE* ME, SIMMONS! I KILLED YOU *ONCE*-- I CAN DO IT *AGAIN!*

YOU STOLE EVERYTHING I CHERISHED! EVERYTHING I LOVED!

TIME I EVENED THE SCORE!

AIGHHGHAA

HERE'S YOUR TRACKING DEVICE. IT WORKS FINE NOW.

YOUR PALS SHOULD FIND YOU SOMETIME.

I WANT TO SEE HOW TOUGH YOU REALLY ARE... IF YOU CAN KEEP THIS WAR ON A PERSONAL LEVEL?

EIGHT HOURS LATER...

CHAPEL!

YOU OKAY?!

HEY, MAN, WHAT HAPPE— JEEZ!

BADROCK, GET THE FIRST AID-- NOW!

HE NEEDS HELP!

CHAPEL-- WHAT'S UP?!

WHERE'S THAT CAPED GUY?

HOW'D YOU GET HERE?

WHAT'D HE WANT? WHAT'D HE SAY?!

MYTHS

WHEREVER HE WENT, THE CITIZENS FLED. THOSE LEFT BEHIND COWERED IN HIS SHADOW.

THIS ISOLATION DROVE HIM MAD.

RIDING ON THE BACK OF HIS BLACK DEMONIC MONSTER, HE INSPIRED OFT-REPEATED STORIES. ONE TOLD OF MEN TRAMPLED, A HUNDRED AT A TIME, JUST SO HE COULD LAUGH AT THEIR BLOOD-CURDLING SCREAMS. CHAOS REIGNED SUPREME. IT WAS SAID THAT HE DERIVED GREAT PLEASURE AS WELL FROM WATCHING OTHERS DO BATTLE-- HIS TWISTED WAY OF UNWINDING. ONE SUCH INCIDENT BROUGHT THE REGION'S RULER OF THAT TIME, KING JOHN IV, INTO CONFLICT WITH A NEIGHBORING TERRITORY.

NO HARM SHALL COME TO THIS TOWN... NOT WHILE I LIVE!

WHILE THE TWO ARMIES STRUGGLED, THE DARK WIZARD STOOD IDLY BY, WATCHING GLEEFULLY AS THE RAPING AND PILLAGING OF EACH TOWN GREW MORE FRENZIED.

HE SEEMED TO TAKE PRIDE IN HIS APATHY.

THE PEOPLE GREW TO HATE HIM MORE AND MORE AS HE STOOD BY DOING NOTHING.

WORD OF MY PRESENCE SPREAD QUICKLY. I SOON VISITED THE SURROUNDING VILLAGES.

I WANTED TO ASSURE THEM ALL PERSONALLY THAT I WAS NOW THEIR SWORN PROTECTOR.

THEY NEEDED NO LONGER FEAR THE EVIL SPAWN-WIZARD.

NOT WHILE I WAS AROUND.

A FEW DAYS LATER, I HEARD OF A MAN WHO HAD BEEN BEATEN BY THE WIZARD, AND YET LIVED.

MORE IMPORTANTLY, HE KNEW WHERE THE WIZARD WAS HEADED. I DID NOT HESITATE TO VISIT THIS POOR, COURAGEOUS MAN.

AFTER GATHERING THE INFORMATION I NEEDED, I MADE SURE THAT HIS WOUNDS WERE PROPERLY TAKEN CARE OF.

NEW YORK CITY'S POLICE DEPARTMENT, 12th PRECINCT...

...SPECIFICALLY, THE OFFICE OF DETECTIVES SAM BURKE AND "TWITCH" WILLIAMS.

P-PLEASE, SIR--!

WATCH THE RIBS.

HELL I FEEL GOOD!

I HOPE CHIEF BANKS IS DYING OF AN ULCER!

WE SHOVED IT RIGHT UP HIS REAR!

GOD BLESS AMERICA!

THEY'VE JUST GOTTEN WORD THAT THEY ARE OFFICIALLY CLEARED OF ANY WRONGDOING, FOLLOWING AN INVESTIGATION INTO THE DEATH OF CHILDKILLER BILLY KINCAID.

THE PAIR CAN NOW RESUME THEIR REGULAR DUTIES ON THE STREETS WITHOUT FURTHER DELAY. TWO WEEKS STRAPPED BEHIND A DESK DROVE SAM ALMOST COMPLETELY BONKERS.

hee-hee-hee!

I LOVE WINNING!

WELL, TWITCH, YOU KNOW WHAT I'M GOING TO DO FIRST, uh?

YES, SIR.

FIND OUR HERO IN THE RED CAPE.

BINGO!

THE INVESTIGATING BOARD DIDN'T KNOW ANYTHING ABOUT HIM. WITH US CLEARED, THEY'RE ANTSY TO FIND OUT WHAT REALLY HAPPENED.

MAYBE WE CAN HELP THEM OUT A BIT.

YES, SIR.

MAY I SUGGEST WE START IMMEDIATELY. I COULD USE A LITTLE OVERTIME.

BY THE WAY, SIR, YOU HAVE A DONUT SQUISHED TO YOUR ASS.

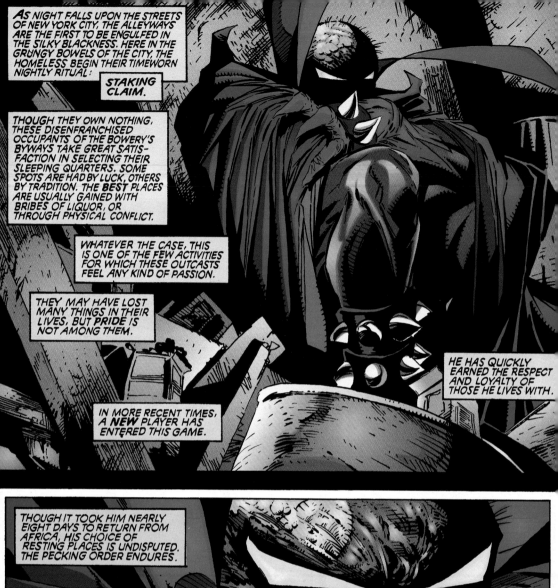

AS NIGHT FALLS UPON THE STREETS OF NEW YORK CITY, THE ALLEYWAYS ARE THE FIRST TO BE ENGULFED IN THE SILKY BLACKNESS. HERE IN THE GRUNGY BOWELS OF THE CITY, THE HOMELESS BEGIN THEIR TIMEWORN NIGHTLY RITUAL:

STAKING CLAIM.

THOUGH THEY OWN NOTHING, THESE DISENFRANCHISED OCCUPANTS OF THE BOWERY'S BYWAYS TAKE GREAT SATIS- FACTION IN SELECTING THEIR SLEEPING QUARTERS. SOME SPOTS ARE HAD BY LUCK, OTHERS BY TRADITION. THE *BEST* PLACES ARE USUALLY GAINED WITH BRIBES OF LIQUOR, OR THROUGH PHYSICAL CONFLICT.

WHATEVER THE CASE, THIS IS ONE OF THE FEW ACTIVITIES FOR WHICH THESE OUTCASTS FEEL ANY KIND OF PASSION.

THEY MAY HAVE LOST MANY THINGS IN THEIR LIVES, BUT *PRIDE* IS NOT AMONG THEM.

HE HAS QUICKLY EARNED THE RESPECT AND LOYALTY OF THOSE HE LIVES WITH.

IN MORE RECENT TIMES, A *NEW* PLAYER HAS ENTERED THIS GAME.

THOUGH IT TOOK HIM NEARLY EIGHT DAYS TO RETURN FROM AFRICA, HIS CHOICE OF RESTING PLACES IS UNDISPUTED. THE PECKING ORDER ENDURES.

SHELTERED AWAY IN HIS NEW RESTING SPOT, SPAWN CAN REFLECT CALMLY ON HIS ACTIONS, CONSIDERING WHAT WENT WRONG, AND WHY.

ANOTHER SLEEPLESS NIGHT. IT'S BECOMING PREDICTABLE.

HOW COULD I BE SO STUPID.

TAKE THE NEXT LEFT, TWITCH. CONNORS SAID THERE'S USUALLY A HIGH DENSITY OF THEM DOWN THAT BACK WAY!

YES, SIR.

I'VE HEARD OUR CAPED VIGILANTE MIGHT BE INVOLVED IN OTHER SLAYINGS.

HOW DO WE KNOW HE'S NOT INVOLVED WITH THE GOVERNMENT'S *YOUNGBLOOD* PROGRAM?

WE *DON'T!*

BUT EVEN IF HE IS, THEY DON'T GIVE PRIVILEGES SUCH AS *MANSLAUGHTER* TO THEIR AGENTS.

WE'VE GOT OURSELVES A PURE AND SIMPLE *WACKO.*

THAT I'LL AGREE WITH, SIR.

GOOD!

NOW LET'S GET GOING. CHANCES ARE, OUR LITTLE HERO'S SPLIT TOWN. IF HE WAS SMART, THAT IS.

BUT I'VE BEEN ONE TO GIVE CRIMINALS ABNORMALLY HIGH I.Q.'S!

WELL, LOOKY WHAT WE'VE GOT HERE. A REGULAR CONVENTION OR SOMETHING. TWITCH, THIS MIGHT JUST BE OUR *LUCKY* DAY.

IT'S NIGHT, SIR.

'EVENING, FELLOWS.

WHOOPEE! IT'S THE FUZZ.

"FUZZ"? SORRY TO BREAK IT TO YOU, BUT THAT TERM WENT OUT FIFTEEN YEARS AGO... THOUGH I DON'T SUPPOSE YOUR STEADY DIET OF *DRUGS* AND *BOOZE* HAS MADE YOU ANY KIND OF EINSTEIN.

PLEASE, SIR. LET'S BE PLEASANT ABOUT THIS.

YOU'RE RIGHT.

GENTLEMEN... MAY I HAVE YOUR ATTENTION *PLEASE!*

MY PARTNER AND I ARE LOOKING FOR A POSSIBLE NEW ACQUAINTANCE OF YOURS. HE WEARS A CAPE, WHICH IS RED. HE CAN SOMEHOW MAKE DEAD BODIES APPEAR IN MY OFFICE.

OTHER THAN THAT, I'M SURE HE'S *PERFECTLY* NORMAL.

RING ANY BELLS?

NOPE.

NOPE.

NOPE.

YOU'RE *NUTS*, COP.

LOST IN THOUGHT, AL TURNS THE CORNER OF THE LONG ALLEYWAY.

QUICKLY, HE SNAPS BACK TO REALITY...

...AND DECIDES TO WANDER AIMLESSLY ELSEWHERE.

NO SENSE IN A CONFRONTATION.

Huh?

WHAT THE *HELL?!*

TWITCH! DID YOU SEE THAT?!

Y-YOU KNOW, NOW THAT YOU ASK, I *DO* REMEMBER--uh--*SOME* GUY THAT-- I THINK HE--

GET OUTTA MY *WAY*, OLD MAN, BEFORE I RUN YOU *OVER!*

SPAWN'S FRIENDS CREATE JUST ENOUGH OF A DISTRACTION TO HELP HIS ESCAPE.

DAMN! HE'S GONE!

*B*ANISHED BY THE DEVIL TO A LIFE ON EARTH IN HUMAN FORM, **THE VIOLATOR** IS AT A LOSS FOR WHAT TO DO NEXT. FACED WITH UNACCUSTOMED SILENCE FROM DOWN BELOW, HE'S BIDING HIS TIME UNTIL HE CAN FIGURE A WAY TO GET BACK HIS LOST POWERS.

NORMALLY A MISSHAPEN EMBODIMENT OF HORROR--WITH PROTRUDING HORNS AND TALONS-- HE IS NOW STUCK IN A THREE-FOOT-TEN-INCH BODY, LOOKING LIKE A MINIATURE SUMO WRESTLER GONE TO SEED... **BAD** SEED. HE IS THE VICTIM OF HIS OWN FAILURE TO FULFILL HIS MASTER'S WISHES. *

ON HIS LAST MISSION, THE VIOLATOR'S ORDERS WERE TO PROVOKE THE NEWLY-ARRIVED **SPAWN** TO EXPERIMENT WITH ITS POWERS. INSTEAD OF STAGING A DIRECT ATTACK, THE VIOLATOR DECIDED TO DRAW THE SPAWN OUT BY GOING ON A KILLING SPREE. BY DISMEMBERING SOME OF NEW YORK'S **TOP MAFIA DONS,** THE VIOLATOR HOPED TO ATTRACT THE MOB AND THE POLICE INTO A TWO-PRONGED ATTACK AGAINST SPAWN, THE NEW, POWERFUL, COSTUMED PLAYER IN THE AREA.

INSTEAD, THE VIOLATOR ONLY COMPLICATED MATTERS. AFTER ALL, THERE WAS NOTHING TO LINK SPAWN WITH THE WEIRDLY BRUTAL KILLINGS. IN FACT, THAT SENSELESS ASSAULT CAUSED THE CRIME CARTEL TO BECOME CAUTIOUS FOR A WHILE. CRIME ACTUALLY WENT **DOWN** A FEW PERCENTAGE POINTS. FROM THE DEVIL'S POINT OF VIEW, THIS WAS **UNACCEPTABLE.** FOR HELL TO PROSPER, EVIL MUST GAIN NEW GROUND, AND THE VIOLATOR WAS TO BLAME FOR THIS SORRY STATE OF DECLINE. AS A PUNISHMENT, THE VIOLATOR HAS LOST ACCESS TO HIS MONSTROUS, MORE POWERFUL FORM.

OUR ROTUND VIOLATOR, THE WORLD-CLASS IDIOT, SIMPLY **DIDN'T GET IT.** FIGURING THAT HE'S MERELY BEEN **REPLACED** BY THE NEW HELLSPAWN, HE DECIDED TO TAKE A REASONED APPROACH AND BUILD SOME SUPPORT AT THE GRASS ROOTS. IF HE CAN IMPRESS THE YOUNG WITH HIS MAGNIFICENT SKILLS AND DEVIL-MAY-CARE PHILOSOPHY, HIS MASTER MAY LOOK KINDLY UPON THE EVENTUAL, DISEASED RESULTS OF HIS INFLUENCE.

CLINT, MARK AND **SPAZ,** THREE CITIZENS OF THE STREETS, HAVE BEEN DRAFTED AS OBSERVERS FOR HIS **ONE-MAN BATTLE OF WITS.**

HE'S BEEN TELLING THEM OF A CAMPAIGN AGAINST **ANOTHER** SPAWN, FOUGHT NEARLY **800 YEARS AGO.** THIS TALE, WE ARE QUICK TO POINT OUT, INVOLVES TWO VICTIMS: THE **SPAWN,** AND THE **FACTS.**

THE VIOLATOR CLEARS HIS THROAT, SPITS IMPRESSIVELY, AND CONTINUES...

*ISSUE № 4 -- Tom·

YOU HEARD ME!! I COMPLETELY **FLAME-BROILED** THE LITTLE **BOOGER!**

IF I BROUGHT THE BOSS THE HEAD OF SPAWN'S WICKED MOTHER, THAT WOULD BE MY EVIDENCE. ONLY IF THE SPAWN WERE TRULY DEAD WOULD I HAVE BEEN ALLOWED TO DECAPITATE THE WITCH HERSELF.

YOUR *GOD* IS MY *ENEMY*.

SO BEG ALL YOU *WANT*.

please...

I HOPE HE'S *LISTENING.*

BECAUSE OF ALL THE PAIN SHE AND HER OFFSPRING HAD BROUGHT TO THE NEIGHBORING LANDS, I WANTED TO MAKE SURE THAT SHE DIED SLOWLY. I WANTED HER TO SUFFER LIKE ALL THOSE INNOCENT VICTIMS HER SON TORTURED.

SO I BEGAN TO CUT HER. SLOWLY.

EEEE

I REJOICED AT EVERY SCREAM, SAVORING THE MOMENT. I COULD ALMOST *TASTE* VICTORY.

...for the love of God...

...I BEG YOU!

BUT SOMETHING WAS WRONG. I COULDN'T QUITE PUT MY *FINGER* ON IT, BUT THIS WAS ALL GOING DOWN FAR TOO EASILY.

PROBABLY MORE TIMES THAN EITHER COULD REMEMBER. EVEN MURDER CAN BECOME TEDIOUS, I SUPPOSE.

WELL, IT WAS HIGH TIME SOMEONE TURNED THE TABLES ON THOSE TWO...

HER COAL-BLACK EYES WITNESSED EVERY MEASURE OF HARM I INFLICTED UPON HER BOY. IT WARMED MY HEART.

HOW MANY TIMES HAD THEY CACKLED SADISTICALLY WHILE STRIPPING THE FLESH FROM A CRYING BABY, I ASKED MYSELF.

...SHOWING THEM FOR THE MONSTERS THEY WERE.

MY PRINCE... WHAT HAVE YOU

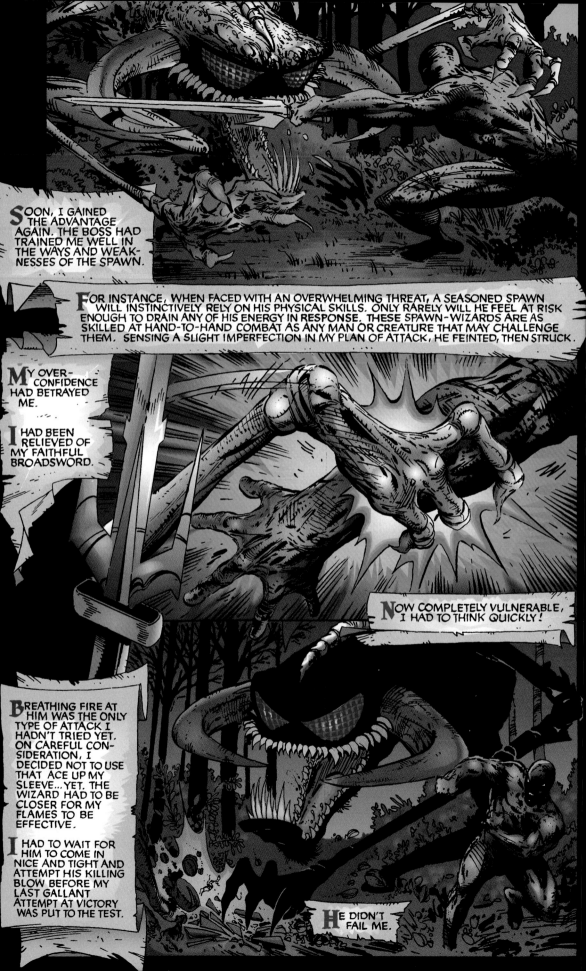

SOON, I GAINED THE ADVANTAGE AGAIN. THE BOSS HAD TRAINED ME WELL IN THE WAYS AND WEAKNESSES OF THE SPAWN.

FOR INSTANCE, WHEN FACED WITH AN OVERWHELMING THREAT, A SEASONED SPAWN WILL INSTINCTIVELY RELY ON HIS PHYSICAL SKILLS. ONLY RARELY WILL HE FEEL AT RISK ENOUGH TO DRAIN ANY OF HIS ENERGY IN RESPONSE. THESE SPAWN-WIZARDS ARE AS SKILLED AT HAND-TO-HAND COMBAT AS ANY MAN OR CREATURE THAT MAY CHALLENGE THEM. SENSING A SLIGHT IMPERFECTION IN MY PLAN OF ATTACK, HE FEINTED, THEN STRUCK.

MY OVER-CONFIDENCE HAD BETRAYED ME.

I HAD BEEN RELIEVED OF MY FAITHFUL BROADSWORD.

NOW COMPLETELY VULNERABLE, I HAD TO THINK QUICKLY!

BREATHING FIRE AT HIM WAS THE ONLY TYPE OF ATTACK I HADN'T TRIED YET. ON CAREFUL CONSIDERATION, I DECIDED NOT TO USE THAT ACE UP MY SLEEVE...YET. THE WIZARD HAD TO BE CLOSER FOR MY FLAMES TO BE EFFECTIVE.

I HAD TO WAIT FOR HIM TO COME IN NICE AND TIGHT AND ATTEMPT HIS KILLING BLOW BEFORE MY LAST GALLANT ATTEMPT AT VICTORY WAS PUT TO THE TEST.

HE DIDN'T FAIL ME.

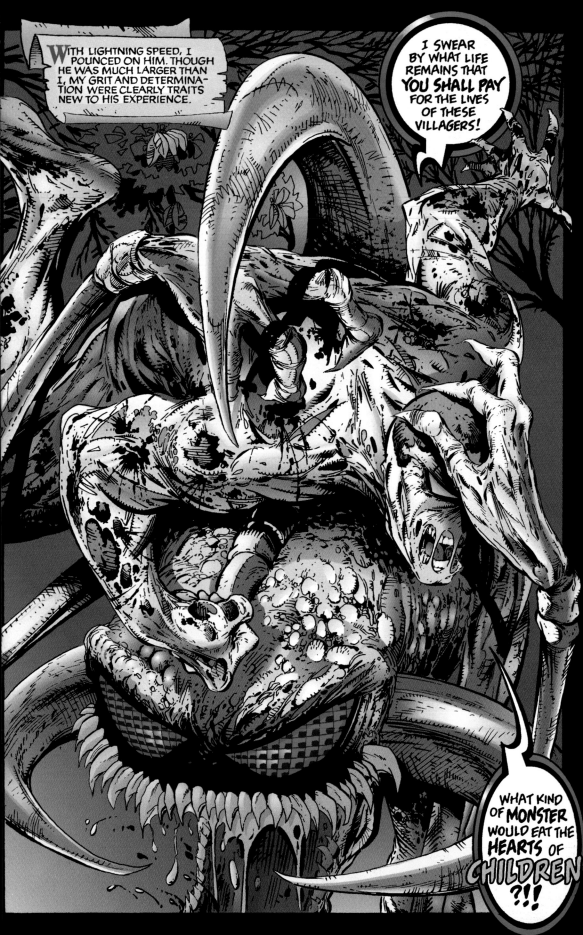

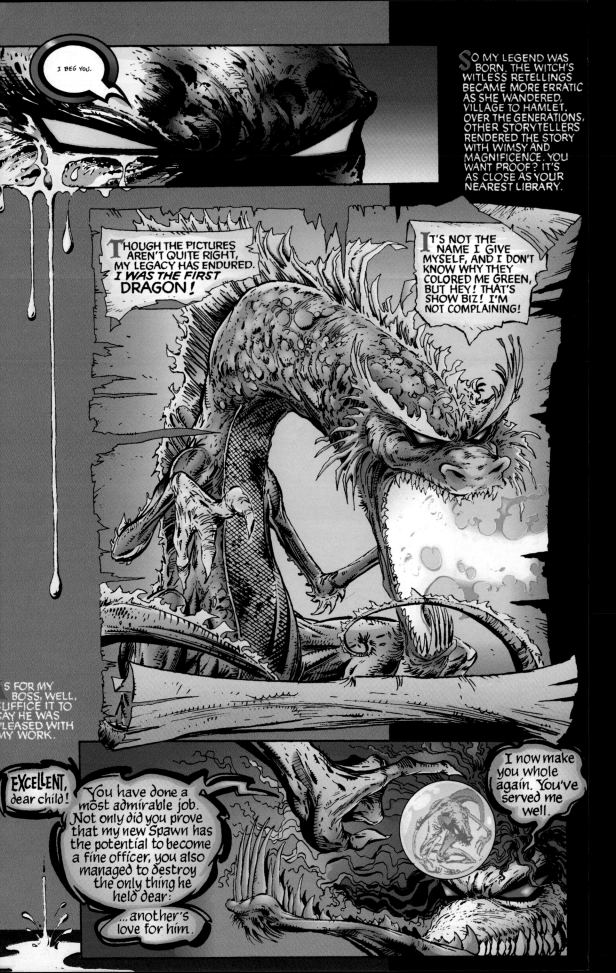

I BEG YOU.

So my legend was born. The witch's witless retellings became more erratic as she wandered, village to hamlet. Over the generations, other storytellers rendered the story with wimsy and magnificence. You want proof? It's as close as your nearest library.

Though the pictures aren't quite right, my legacy has endured. I WAS THE FIRST DRAGON!

It's not the name I give myself, and I don't know why they colored me green, but hey! That's show biz! I'm not complaining!

As for my boss, well, suffice it to say he was pleased with my work.

Excellent, dear child! You have done a most admirable job. Not only did you prove that my new Spawn has the potential to become a fine officer, you also managed to destroy the only thing he held dear:

...another's love for him.

I now make you whole again. You've served me well.

67

"ESPECIALLY NOT THAT PUNK, *SPAWN.*"*

THOUGH IT IS NO LONGER AS NECESSARY AS IT HAD BEEN, *AL SIMMONS,* STRICTLY BY HABIT, RESTS DAILY. HIS NEW CIRCUMSTANCE, AS AN AGENT OF EVIL FROM DEEP IN THE BOWELS OF SOME NETHERWORLD, HASN'T ERASED HIS HUMANISTIC SELF-IMAGE.

HABITS -- ROUTINES -- IN THESE NEW TIMES, THEY ARE HIS ONLY SOURCE FOR *TRANQUILITY...*

... IF YOU WILL, FOR *ESCAPE.*

SLEEP.

HEY, BUD!

HOW MANY TIMES I GOTTA *TELL* YOU CREEPS TO *STAY AWAY* FROM THE *BACK DOOR!*

*FOR DETAILS OF THE VIOLATOR'S VISIT TO TONY TWIST'S OFFICE, SEE THE VIOLATOR'S OWN MINI-SERIES, COMING IN 1994. --Tom.

YA *HEAR ME?!*

I'M GETTING FRIGGIN' *TIRED* OF YOU TRYING TO STEAL THE FOOD SCRAPS FROM MR. NUNOZ'S RESTAURANT. THOUGHT I MADE MYSELF *CLEAR* LAST TIME.

YOU MUST BE THE *DEAF* ONE OF THE BUNCH!

URRK

OKAY!

OKAY! TAKE IT *EASY.* NO SENSE GETTING IN SUCH A BIG *HUFF.* I'LL BE OUT OF YOUR WAY IN A MINUTE.

DIDN'T KNOW SOMEONE COULD TAKE SUCH *PRIDE* IN PROTECTING SCRAPS OF LEFT-OVER LIVER.

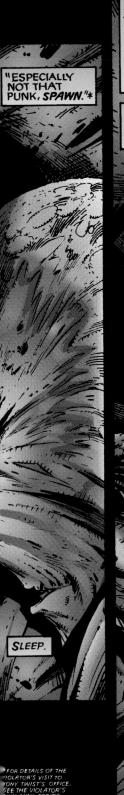

"WE KNOW YOU'VE BEEN *MESSING* WITH US, FITZGERALD. NO ONE LIKES A *RAT*.

"SO YOU'D BETTER BE A VERY GOOD BOY AND HOPE WE DON'T FIND NOTHING *INCRIMINATING*.

WELL, GOTTA *GO* NOW. KISS THAT BEAUTIFUL WIFE OF YOURS FOR ME. SHE SURE IS A LOOKER. I'VE BEEN *WATCHING* HER FOR ALMOST *THREE WEEKS* NOW. PRETTY SEXY *NIGHTGOWN* SHE'S BEEN WEARING.

YOU SONUVABITCH.

"'CAUSE IF WE *DO*, THERE AIN'T *NO* PLACE YOU'RE GOING TO BE ABLE TO HIDE FROM US. AND WHEN WE FIND YOU, WORDS CAN'T DESCRIBE THE KIND OF *PAIN* WE CAN INFLICT.

NOW NOW, TERRY. IT'S A DIRTY JOB, BUT SOME-ONE'S GOT TO DO IT.

KISS THAT *BABY* OF YOURS FOR ME, TOO.

CLICK

IT WILL BE NEARLY TWENTY MINUTES BEFORE TERRY MOVES...

...ANOTHER FORTY BEFORE HE STOPS SWEATING.

NEXT ISSUE:

GRANT **MORRISON**

GREG **CAPULLO**

"FLASHBACK" PART ONE

Todd McFarlane – *story & art*

Tom Orzechowski – *letters & editor*

Steve Oliff, Reuben Rude and Olyoptics – *colour*

"FLASHBACK" PART TWO

Todd McFarlane – *story & art*

Tom Orzechowski – *letters & editor*

Steve Oliff, Reuben Rude and Olyoptics – *colour*

"MYTHS" PART ONE

Todd McFarlane – *story & art*

Tom Orzechowski – *letters & editor*

Steve Oliff, Reuben Rude and Olyoptics – *colour*

"MYTHS" PART TWO

Todd McFarlane – *story & art*

Tom Orzechowski – *letters & editor*

Steve Oliff, Reuben Rude and Olyoptics – *colour*

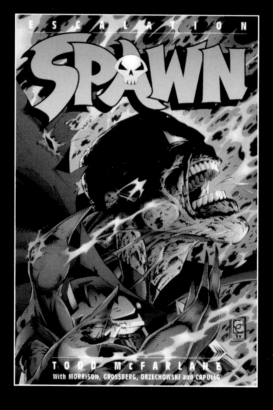